KIERAN'S KARATE ADVENTURE

Popcorn
ELT
Readers

Kieran

Kieran is twelve years old. He loves karate! He started karate classes when he was eight years old.

Kieran's mum

Kieran's mum has a cafe. Kieran sometimes helps her there.

Riley

Riley is in Kieran's class a school. He doesn't know anything about karate.

The dojo

Kieran learns karate moves in the dojo. *Dojo* is the Japanese word for karate school.

punch   **reverse punch**   **kick**   **block**

Sensei Matsumi

Sensei* Matsumi knows a lot about karate. But who is he?

Miss Moon

Miss Moon is Kieran's karate teacher. She is also a teacher at his school.

Before you read ...
What do you think? Are Kieran and Riley friends?

Sensei is the Japanese word for teacher.

New Words

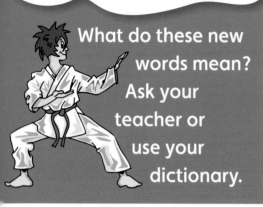

What do these new words mean? Ask your teacher or use your dictionary.

calm

The water was very **calm**.

bow

They are **bowing**.

competition

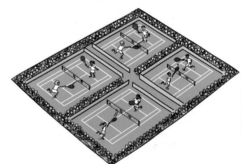

There were a lot of people in the **competition**.

breathe in / out

Breathe in!

dragon

This is a **dragon**.

dream

He has a **dream**. / He is **dreaming**.

ready

I'm ready!

fight

The girls are **fighting**.

remember

I **remember** my first day at school.

medal

They won **medals**!

'Respect!'

Respect!

Verbs

Present	Past
fight	fought
wake up	woke up
win	won

What does the title *Kieran's Karate Adventure* mean?

Ask your teacher.

KIERAN'S KARATE ADVENTURE

CHAPTER ONE
'Stay calm, Kieran!'

Kieran loved Fridays. On Fridays he had his karate class! Kieran was a blue belt. He wanted to be a brown belt, but it was a lot of work.

Kieran bowed to his teacher. 'Thank you, Sensei.'

'That was good work, Kieran,' Miss Moon said. 'See you at school on Monday!'

Miss Moon was also a teacher at Kieran's school.

Riley and his friends were in Kieran's class at school. They watched him and laughed.

'Ha, ha! He's bowing!'

'Hey, Kieran!' Riley said when Kieran came out. 'I like your trousers!'

Kieran said nothing. He didn't like Riley.

'Thank you, Miss Moon! I love you, Miss Moon!'
Riley laughed.

Now Kieran couldn't walk away. He jumped
onto Riley and the boys started to fight.

'Stop!' It was Miss Moon. 'What are you doing?
Riley! Why are you here? Go home!'

She looked at Kieran. 'You too, Kieran! No
fighting outside the dojo. You know that!'

Kieran walked home. His mum worked in a cafe in the town and they lived above it.

'Hi! How was karate?' she asked when he came in.

'I had a fight with Riley after the class,' Kieran said.

'Not again!' his mum said. 'Why are you always fighting with that boy?'

Kieran went to read in his bedroom, but he was very tired. His eyes started to close, but then he saw an old man in front of him.

'I am Sensei Matsumi,' the man said. 'Don't be frightened. I am here to help you. Stay calm, Kieran!'

'Calm? What ...?' Kieran wanted to ask more but the man wasn't there now.

'Maybe it was a dream,' Kieran thought.

CHAPTER TWO
'No more fighting!'

There were always a lot of people in the cafe on Saturdays. Sometimes Kieran helped his mum.

'Look, Kieran,' she said. 'Is that your karate teacher?'

'Hello!' Miss Moon said. 'I want to talk to you about something ...'

'Oh no,' thought Kieran. 'She's going to talk about my fight with Riley.'

'There's a karate competition in four weeks,' said Miss Moon. 'Do you want to be in it?'

'Me?' said Kieran.

'Why not?' said Miss Moon. 'You're a good student. There are four karate classes every week. The first class is after school on Monday.'

'No problem!' said Kieran.

'It's not going to be easy,' Miss Moon looked at him. 'And no more fighting at school.'

In school on Monday morning, Kieran didn't look at Riley. Kieran was good at drawing and he had a new picture. It was a red dragon. 'That's cool!' he thought. He went to find some different pens.

'Watch this!' Riley said to his friends. When Kieran came back, he saw Riley's writing on his picture. 'I LOVE MISS MOON! XXX'.

'That's NOT funny, Riley!' he shouted.

Miss Moon looked up. 'Is there a problem?' she asked.

'No, Miss Moon,' said Kieran. His face was red.

Kieran didn't want to think about Riley. He wanted to think about his karate. After school, he went to his new class.

'Reverse punch!' shouted Miss Moon. 'One more time.'

But Kieran was tired. 'When are we going to start fighting?' he thought.

'Kieran! Forty press-ups!' Miss Moon said.

Later Kieran fought with a new blue belt, but he didn't win.

'You need to work more,' said Miss Moon.

That night Kieran dreamed of Sensei Matsumi again. 'When you are angry,' the sensei said, 'you do not fight well.'

CHAPTER THREE
'Are you ready?'

In the karate classes, Kieran blocked, kicked and punched ... again and again.

In one class, he fought with Miss Moon. 'Good work,' she said. 'On Saturday you can fight with Terry G.'

After class, Miss Moon gave Kieran a book. 'It's old,' she said, 'but it's interesting. Karate is not only about fighting. I want you to read it and think about things. Do you understand?'

'Maybe,' said Kieran.

When Kieran saw Terry G, he wanted to run away. Terry G was tall like Kieran but he was also very strong.

'Aiiieee!' shouted Terry G. He ran at Kieran.

'Oh no!' thought Kieran. He didn't win the fight.

That night, Kieran had a bad dream. A red dragon jumped in front of him. He was very frightened. He couldn't move. Then Sensei Matsumi was there again.

'You didn't win the fight because you were frightened,' said Sensei Matsumi.

'I'm not frightened!' shouted Kieran angrily and he woke up. 'I'm NOT!'

When Kieran walked to school the next day, he looked at Miss Moon's book. 'Do not be the first to fight,' the book said. 'It is better to move away than fight.'

Riley and his friends waited outside school.

'Hey, karate boy!' Riley shouted. 'Let's see you fight!'

Kieran closed his eyes. 'One … two … three …' he said slowly. When he opened his eyes, Riley was not there.

That night Kieran dreamed of Riley and Terry
G. They were dragons. The two dragons ran
at him but he stayed calm. He thought quickly.
He stopped and did a reverse punch on one
dragon. Quickly he kicked the other dragon.

Kieran moved away and the two dragons
started to fight.

Then Kieran saw Sensei Matsumi. 'Are you
ready now, Kieran?' he asked.

CHAPTER FOUR
'Go, Kieran!'

It was the day of the competition. There were a lot of people there. Kieran waited quietly. He looked around. His mum was next to Miss Moon. And behind them was … Oh no! It was Riley.

'Stay calm,' thought Kieran. He closed his eyes and breathed in and out slowly. When the competition started, he was ready.

Kieran remembered everything from his karate classes. He remembered Sensei Matsumi's words. He punched and kicked and blocked.

'Go, Kieran!' shouted his friends from school. It was fun.

At the end of the competition, Miss Moon gave out the medals. And Kieran won silver!

When Kieran walked out of the school that
night, Riley was outside. He came up to Kieran.

'Respect!' he said. 'That was cool.'

'Thanks!' said Kieran.

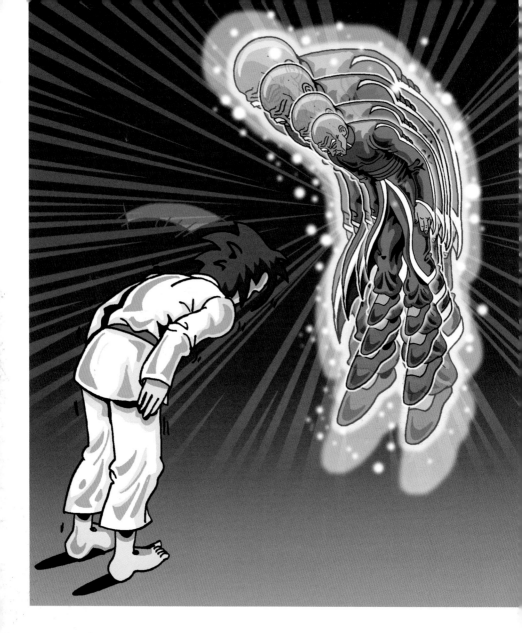

That night, Kieran looked at Miss Moon's karate book before he went to sleep. Sensei Matsumi was there in his dreams. Sensei Matsumi bowed and Kieran bowed back. Then suddenly Sensei Matsumi was very small and far away.

When Kieran woke up, he saw the old karate book. It was open. There was a picture of an old sensei on the page.

'Wow!' said Kieran. 'I know that face. It's Sensei Matsumi!'

THE END

LEARN KARATE!

Karate is a martial art from Asia. Many millions of people around the world learn karate.

In the dojo

Karate students (*karatakas*) do not wear shoes in the dojo. The class starts with a short meditation. Then the *karatakas* bow to the sensei and to the other students in the class. Students also bow at the start of a fight.

suit
belt

Did you know?

The sensei speaks Japanese in class. Karate means 'empty hand'.

空手

kara = empty

te = hand

Karate belts

Karatakas wear a white suit with a coloured belt. When you start karate, you have a white belt. A blue belt knows all the basic kicks, punches and blocks. Black belts are the highest level. You can only be a sensei when you have a black belt.

Be careful!

If you do not work well in class, the sensei can ask you to do press-ups!

What do these words mean? Find out.

martial art   meditation   empty
rule   show respect

Show respect

Karate is not only about fighting. It is also about thinking. Sensei Gichin Funakoshi (1868 – 1957) made twenty rules for karate today. One of the rules is: always show respect for other people.

★

Would you like to learn karate? Why / Why not?

★

After you read

1 Match the names and the sentences.

a) Kieran
b) Kieran's mum
c) Riley
d) Sensei Matsumi
e) Miss Moon

i) She gives a book to Kieran.
ii) He's in Kieran's class.
iii) She has a cafe.
iv) He helps Kieran.
v) He loves karate!

2 Put the sentences in order.

a) Kieran started his new karate class. ☐
b) Kieran dreamed about a red dragon. ☐
c) Kieran fought with Terry G. ☐
d) Miss Moon came to the cafe. ☐
e) Kieran had a fight with Riley. 1
f) Kieran won a silver medal. ☐
g) Miss Moon gave Kieran an old book. ☐
h) Kieran saw Sensei Matsumi for the first time. ☐

Where's the popcorn!
Look in your book. Can you find it?

Puzzle time!

1a Can you find out the message? Who says this in *Kieran's Karate Adventure*?

19–20–1–25

__ __ __ __

3–1–12–13

__ a __ __ !

b Now write a message to a friend.

2 Answer the questions. Use the adjectives below.

ANGRY   calm   *frightened*   HAPPY   tired

How do you feel if ...
a) ... you have a bad dream? frightened
b) ... you can't sleep? ....
c) ... you see a very big dog? ....
d) ... you are in a very noisy room? ....
e) ... breathe in and out slowly? ....
f) ... your teacher doesn't give
    you any homework? ....

3 Find the letters. What word do the letters spell?

a) What colour is Kieran's medal? Write the last letter.

□

b) What colour is Kieran's karate belt? Write the last letter.

□

c) What's this animal? Write the third letter of its name.

□

d) What is this boy doing? Write the first letter of the verb.

d

e) Write the last letter of this boy's name.

□

4 Draw Kieran's picture of a red dragon.

1 Work in pairs. Invent mimes for the following
words and phrases.

Stay calm!

Stop and think!

Breathe in!

*It is better to move
away than fight.*

Remember!

2 Now work with another pair. Show them your
mimes. Can they copy them?

1 🎵 **Listen and read.**

Kieran's chant

CHORUS
Kick, block, punch.
Kick, block, punch.

Kieran's very angry.
He fights at school.

Kieran does karate.
He has to work and work.

It's the competition!
And Kieran is ready.

Kieran stops.
Kieran thinks.

Kieran wins silver.
Respect!

2 🎵 **Say the chant.**